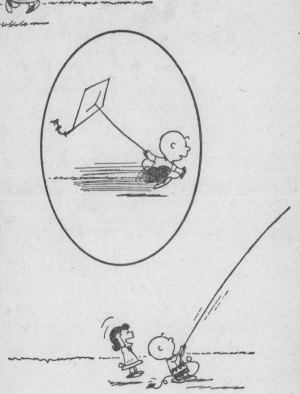

You're My Hero,

A FAWCETT CREST BOOK

Fawcett Publications, Inc., Greenwich, Conn.

Member of American Book Publishers Council, Inc.

— Charlie Brown!

Selected Cartoons from PEANUTS EVERY SUNDAY VOL.2

by CHARLES M. SCHULZ

Other Peanuts Books in Fawcett Crest Editions:

This book, prepared especially for Fawcett Publications, Inc., comprises the second half of PEANUTS EVERY SUNDAY, and is reprinted by arrangement with Holt, Rinehart and Winston, Inc.

Second Fawcett Crest Printing, September 1968

Published by Fawcett World Library
67 West 44th Street, New York, N. Y. 10036
Printed in the United States of America

IF YOU CAN'T TRUST DOGS AND LITTLE BABIES, WHOM CAN YOU TRUST?

OF ALL THE STUPID **HABITS**, THAT BLANKET IS THE **STUPIDEST**! AND THAT'S ALL IT IS, JUST A **HABIT**! A STUPID **HABIT**!!

YOU'RE NOT GOING TO TEACH HER TO USE A BLANKET FOR SECURITY OR FOR HAPPINESS OR FOR **ANYTHING**! SALLY IS GOING TO USE HER OWN WILL-POWER TO GROW FROM A BABY TO A **WELL-ADJUSTED CHILD** !!!!

LIKE HER BROTHER?

SIGH

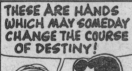

OKAY, CHARLIE BROWN... LET'S GIVE HIM THE OL' FAST ONE... LET'S THROW IT RIGHT BY HIM!

WELL, WHAT **ELSE** CAN WE USE FOR HOME PLATE?

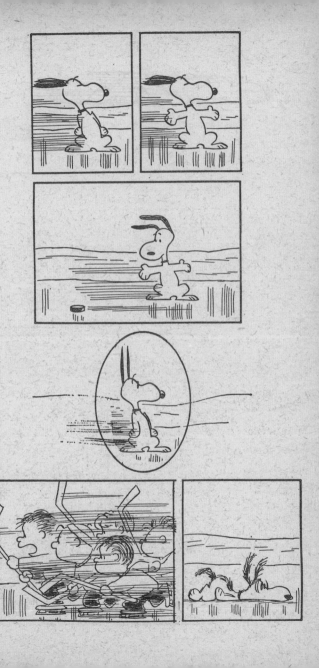

BUT THAT'S THE WHOLE IDEA, CHARLIE BROWN.. THE ODDS NOW ARE REALLY IN YOUR FAVOR!

ONE OF THESE TIMES I MAY **NOT** JERK THE BALL AWAY! ONE OF THESE TIMES I MAY ACTUALLY HOLD ON TO IT!

I NEVER THOUGHT OF IT THAT WAY...

OKAY...YOU HOLD THE BALL, AND I'LL COME RUNNING UP, AND KICK IT!

AAUGH!

WHAM

I'M SORRY...THIS WASN'T THE TIME!

WHOMP!

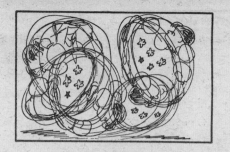

☆ POW! WHAM! ☆

BANG
WHAP! POW!
SOCKO!
OUCH! OOF!
LEGGO!
YIPE!

YOU'VE GOT TO SAY TO YOURSELF "I BELIEVE THAT I CAN FLY THIS KITE"

NOW, GO AHEAD... SAY TO YOURSELF, "I BELIEVE THAT I CAN FLY THIS KITE!"

I BELIEVE THAT I CAN FLY THIS KITE

ALL RIGHT, NOW SAY IT OUT LOUD... SAY IT OVER AND OVER...

I BELIEVE THAT I CAN FLY THIS KITE! I BELIEVE THAT I CAN FLY THIS KITE!

I ACTUALLY BELIEVE THAT I CAN FLY THIS KITE!

YOU DO?

I'LL BET YOU TEN-TO-ONE YOU'RE WRONG!

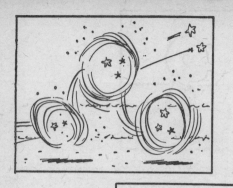

IS THIS ALL YOU HAVE TO DO? ARE YOU GOING TO SPEND THE WHOLE DAY SLIDING BACK AND FORTH ON A PIECE OF ICE?!

DO YOU THINK THESE DAYS WERE GIVEN TO YOU TO WASTE? DOESN'T LIFE MEAN MORE TO YOU THAN THIS?!

IT ALWAYS COMES AS A SHOCK WHEN IT HAPPENS TO SOMEONE YOU KNOW...

DO YOU WANNA SEE A KID WITH A GREAT THROWING ARM?

THERE'S A KID WITH A GREAT THROWING ARM!

ALL RIGHT, YOU'VE WATCHED THAT PROGRAM LONG ENOUGH...NOW, I WANT TO WATCH MY PROGRAM!

CLICK

AAUGH!

I CAN'T STAND IT!

WHAT A STRUGGLE...IT TOOK ME FORTY-FIVE MINUTES TO LAND HIM!

THUMP!

WHAT DO YOU HAVE THERE, CHARLIE BROWN?

I'VE WRITTEN A POEM..

REALLY? READ IT..

ALL RIGHT.. IT ISN'T VERY LONG..

SOME DAYS YOU THINK MAYBE YOU KNOW EVERYTHING...SOME DAYS YOU THINK MAYBE YOU DON'T KNOW ANYTHING... SOME DAYS YOU THINK YOU KNOW A FEW THINGS...SOME DAYS YOU DON'T EVEN KNOW HOW OLD YOU ARE.

YOU CAN'T THROW ME OUT OF MY OWN HOUSE!

I LIVE HERE, TOO, YOU KNOW! YOU'LL NEVER GET AWAY WITH THIS! DO YOU HEAR ME?!!

SHE DRIVES ME CRAZY! I'M SO MAD I FEEL LIKE I'M GOING TO EXPLODE!!

I DON'T HAVE TO STAND FOR THIS! I DON'T HAVE TO TAKE THIS FROM HER!

I'M GOING TO TELL HER OFF LIKE SHE'S NEVER BEEN TOLD OFF BEFORE!

SLAM!

WELL?

I HOPE YOU DON'T GET **ANYTHING** YOU WANT FOR CHRISTMAS!

I'LL LOSE MY MIND BEFORE THIS DAY IS OVER!

TRY NOT TO THINK ABOUT IT...

I CAN'T HELP THINKING ABOUT IT!

I'M ONLY HUMAN!

OH, HOW I HATE MONDAYS!

RELAX!

HOW CAN I RELAX WITH MY BLANKET IN THE WASH? WHY DOES SHE HAVE TO WASH IT ANYWAY?! IT WASN'T VERY DIRTY!

I GOTTA HAVE THAT BLANKET!

TUM DE DA.. DE DUM DE DA DE DUM DE DA

WHAM!

OH, CUT IT OUT!

WELL, THEY **ARE**!

WHAT ABOUT THAT LITTLE KID LAST YEAR WHO WOULDN'T SAY HIS PIECE? HE WOULDN'T EVEN GET OFF HIS MOTHER'S LAP! HE WAS SCARED! HE WAS REALLY SCARED!

AND WHAT ABOUT THAT LITTLE BLONDE GIRL WHO STARTED TO CRY WHEN EVERYONE ELSE WAS SINGING? DON'T TELL ME THAT ISN'T WRONG!

I'M REVOLTING AGAINST CHRISTMAS PROGRAMS!!

LOOK...DO YOU SEE THIS? WHAT IS IT?

IT'S MY PART IN THE CHRISTMAS PROGRAM...I'M SUPPOSED TO MEMORIZE IT..

ALL RIGHT...NOW DO YOU SEE THIS? WHAT IS THIS?

IT'S A FIST!

"AND IT CAME TO PASS IN THOSE DAYS, THAT THERE WENT OUT A DECREE FROM CAESAR AUGUSTUS, THAT ALL THE WORLD SHOULD BE TAXED..."

THIS IS A SCULPTURE WHICH STANDS IN THE LITTLE GARDEN JUST BEHIND THE HOUSE..

HERE I AM AGAIN POSING BY THE HOUSE

WILL THESE PICTURES BE WORTH A LOT OF MONEY SOMEDAY?

I DOUBT IT..

I DON'T SEE HOW ANYBODY CAN SAVE SOMETHING THAT WON'T BE WORTH A LOT OF MONEY SOMEDAY..

And don't forget about all the other PEANUTS books in the new Fawcett Crest editions. Good Grief! More than 26 million of them in paperback!

© 1967 United Feature Syndicate, Inc.

D1097	WHO DO YOU THINK YOU ARE, CHARLIE BROWN?	**D1129**	GOOD GRIEF, CHARLIE BROWN
D1070	GOOD OL' SNOOPY	**D1128**	HEY, PEANUTS!
D1142	VERY FUNNY, CHARLIE BROWN	**D1115**	THE WONDERFUL WORLD OF PEANUTS
D1140	WHAT NEXT, CHARLIE BROWN!	**D1113**	HERE COMES CHARLIE BROWN
D1134	YOU ARE TOO MUCH, CHARLIE BROWN	**D1105**	WE'RE ON YOUR SIDE, CHARLIE BROWN
D1141	FOR THE LOVE OF PEANUTS!	**D1099**	HERE COMES SNOOPY
D1130	YOU'RE A WINNER, CHARLIE BROWN	**D1096**	LET'S FACE IT, CHARLIE BROWN

D1133 FUN WITH PEANUTS

Wherever Paperbacks Are Sold

Buy these Fawcett Crest Books from your paperback bookseller. If he is sold out, send only price of books pl 10¢ each for postage and handling to Fawcett Publications, Greenwich, Conn. If order is for fi or more books, no postage or handling charge is necessary. Please order by number and title. No Canadian order